D1298306

THIS BOOK BELONGS TO

KEEP OUT

CHECK IT OUT!

Keep track of the pages you have filled in by checking them off here!

STICK A PHOTO OF
YOURSELF HERE!

NAME:

AGE:

BIRTHDAY:

ADDRESS:

PHONE NUMBER:

E-MAIL ADDRESS:

IT'S ALL ABOUT DETAILS ...

Eye color: _____

Hair color: _____

Height: _____

Nickname: _____

How I got my nickname: _____

People tell me I look like ...

_____

_____

_____

I have [　　　] sisters and [　　　] brothers.

THE BEST STUFF

The best things on the planet
include (but are not limited to):

DRAW IT HERE

BEST Sports:

BEST Animal:

BEST Time of day:

BEST Clothes:

BEST Season:

BEST Food:

BEST Drink:

6

BEST Book: _____

_____

BEST TV show: _____

_____

BEST Movie: _____

_____

BEST Magazine: _____

_____

BEST Joke: _____

_____

_____

DRAW IT HERE →

BEST Thing to do on the weekend: _____

_____

BEST Thing to do indoors: _____

_____

BEST Thing to do outdoors: _____

_____

_____

BEST Superhero: _____

BEST Video game: _____

BEST Band/musician: _____

THE WORST STUFF

Things that annoy me most on the planet include (but are not limited to):

NOTE: Make sure these things are kept away from me!

↙ DRAW IT HERE

WORST Animal: _____

WORST Sports: _____

WORST Clothes: _____

WORST Time of day: _____

WORST Season: _____

WORST Food: _____

WORST Drink: _____

(WORST) Book: _____

(WORST) TV show: _____

(WORST) Movie: _____

(WORST) Magazine: _____

(WORST) Joke: _____

DRAW IT HERE

(WORST) Superhero: _____

(WORST) Thing to do on the weekend: _____

(WORST) Thing to do indoors: _____

(WORST) Thing to do outdoors: _____

(WORST) Video game: _____

(WORST) Band/musician: _____

9

THE AWARD

The people in your world are pretty amazing and crazy at the same time. Award the certificates below to those who deserve them!

This award is presented to

_____

for being

my BEST FRIEND ever

This award is presented to

_____

for being

the BEST BURPER!

This award is presented to

_____

for having

AWESOME STYLE

SHOW

This award is presented to

_____

for being
the **CRAZIEST** person
I know

This award is presented to

_____

for being
aMaZingly artistic

This award is presented to

_____

for being the
CLASS CLOWN

This award is presented to

_____

for having
insane gamer skills

This award is presented to

_____

for being
the most **annoying** person ever

PINBOARD

Cut out scraps from magazines or draw the things you want, the things you love, or just things that are totally sick right now!

MY SECRET, SECRET FILE

My secret wish: _____

_____

_____

I'm embarrassed to admit that I: _____

_____

_____

Secretly, the girl that I kinda like: _____

_____

I would never admit to my friends: _____

_____

_____

My secret favorite TV show: _____

_____

My secret favorite movie: _____

_____

TOP SECRET

LEVEL 1
SECURITY
CLEARENCE

TOP SECRET

My worst habit: _____

_____

_____

_____

My parents have known me for a long time ... They have many
embarrassing stories to tell, and I hope that they never tell this
one ... (Write your most embarrassing memory.)

_____

_____

_____

_____

_____

_____

_____

_____

_____

FOR YOUR

CAUTION: DO NOT

FORT ME

My room is the most secret place of all (except for my brain!).

This is the layout of my room:
(Don't forget to mark down any hiding places or favorite spots so you don't forget them later)

SPECIFICALLY:
NO GIRLS ALLOWED!

ROOM RENDEZVOUS

The best thing about my room:

_____

_____

_____

_____

_____

My favorite thing to do in my room:

_____

_____

_____

_____

If I could change my room I would:

_____

_____

_____

_____

_____

_____

TEST YOURSELF

Keep a record of your test results here.

TEST	ATTEMPT 1	ATTEMPT 2	ATTEMPT 3
Speed-read one page			
Spin a basketball on one finger			
Sit-ups in one go			
Keep the soccer ball off the ground			
Run laps			
Push-ups in one go			

Be the best you can be!

CAUTION DO NOT READ

Create your own tests!

TEST	ATTEMPT 1	ATTEMPT 2	ATTEMPT 3

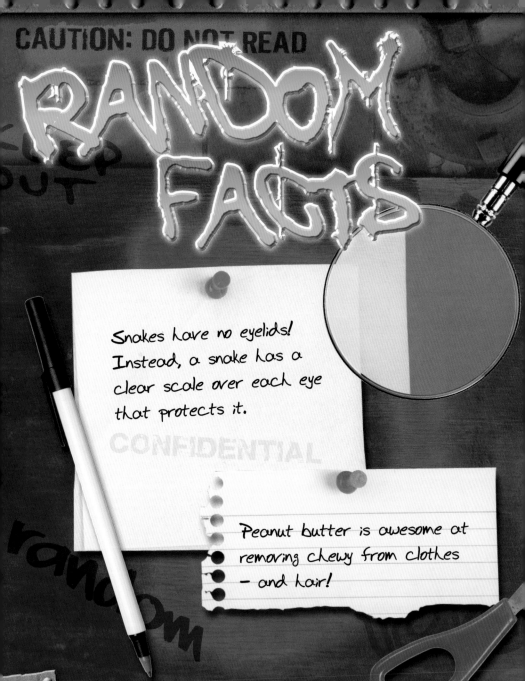

CAUTION: DO NOT READ

RANDOM FACTS

Snakes have no eyelids!
Instead, a snake has a
clear scale over each eye
that protects it.

CONFIDENTIAL

Peanut butter is awesome at
removing chewy from clothes
– and hair!

It is impossible to sneeze with your eyes open.

You can hang upside down when eating, but your food will still travel to your stomach. That's a bit of an uphill climb!

A turtle can breathe through its butt. Ew ...

RANDOM FACTS

The Nile River in Africa is the longest river in the world ... How long do you think it would take you to travel all 4,200 miles of it??

Tooth enamel is the hardest substance that your body makes!

A jellyfish can sting you even after it has died ...

Did you know that sound travels faster in water than it does in air?

Plants store the energy they get from the sun in their leaves.

Sunflowers turn very slowly so they are always facing the sun — clever flower!

Want to make something that feels quite disgusting? Then grab the ingredients below and go!

Ingredients:

1 cup cornflour

1/2 cup water

food coloring

It's as simple as mixing all the ingredients together! Great for squeezing through your hands (or chasing after someone with).

Be careful – some people may get snotty if they get some of your glook on them!

gIRL-PROOF yOUR ROOM

Don't expect girls to just **KNOW** that they are not allowed in your boy-only space. Sometimes you have to take some precautions to make sure it remains she-free...

1. Make a sign to put on your door — this way it is obvious! Draw the sign you plan to use below.

2. Girls make a habit of hiding secret things under their bed or their mattress. Use your imagination to find NEW places to hide your secret things (like this journal).

3. If there are no places to hide your things, you can make them. Tape a folder underneath your desk. No one will be able to see it unless they crawl under there. It will be the perfect place to hide secret notes and maps.

BE CAREFUL!
The most dangerous thing about hiding your stuff away is that you might not remember where you put it! Create yourself a coded map or list so you can remind yourself of all your hot spots. By writing it in code it means that you can keep it in the open – and no one will be able to decipher it! (See pages 32–33 for hints on how to create a code.)

EVER DREAMT OF BEING A SPY? WELL, READ ON AND YOU WILL GET SOME OF THE BEST TIPS EVER TO GET YOUR SPY CAREER STARTED ...

TOOLS EVERY SPY NEEDS:

- A MAGNIFYING GLASS (YOU NEVER KNOW HOW SMALL A CLUE MAY BE)
- SMALL NOTEPAD AND PEN/PENCIL (WRITE DOWN DETAILS AS SOON AS YOU DISCOVER THEM!)
- DECODER (TO DECIPHER ANY NOTES LEFT FOR YOU BY YOUR SIDEKICK)
- VARIOUS DISGUISES (THESE CAN INCLUDE GLASSES, WIGS, AND HATS)
- WATCH (FOR STAKEOUTS AND NOTING TIME IN YOUR NOTEBOOK)
- SCOTCH TAPE (TO LIFT AND STORE FINGERPRINTS)

NOTE: One of the most important skills a spy needs to learn is how to be inconspicuous (this means that you don't stand out). When you have this skill, you can follow your clues without giving yourself away.

MY BEST DISGUISE: _____

USE THE SPACE BELOW TO DRAW (OR STICK A PHOTO) OF YOUR BEST DISGUISE. _____

TIPS: Write all your clues down – no matter how small! This way when you have to go over the evidence later, you'll have it all available and you won't miss a single clue.

Practice all forms of code. You can create your own or study available ones such as Morse code. This will make you sharper should you come across your suspect's codes and also means you can leave notes behind for your partner in secret!

People leave behind fingerprints everywhere. You can lift a fingerprint off glass to store for evidence by using Scotch tape over the fingerprint. Keep the piece of tape in your notebook for reference.

Clues come in all shapes and sizes. This list can include: footprints, fingerprints, hair, lipstick on drinking glasses, scraps of paper ...

IF YOU PLAN TO BE A GREAT SPY, YOU NEED TO BE ABLE TO **SPEAK** IN CODE AS WELL AS WRITE IN CODE. ONE OF THE BEST VERBAL CODES USED BY SPIES IS CALLED PIG-LATIN.

THE WAY TO SPEAK THIS SECRET CODE IS TO TAKE THE INITIAL CONSONANT SOUND AT THE BEGINNING OF THE WORD AND PLACE IT AT THE END AND THEN ADD 'AY' TO THAT FIRST LETTER.

FOR EXAMPLE:

'DOG' BECOMES 'OG-DAY' BECAUSE WE HAVE TAKEN THE FIRST LETTER (D), MOVED IT TO THE END AND THEN ADDED 'AY' AFTER IT.

CONFIDENTIAL

LATIN

PRIVATE

More examples:

'PRANK' BECOMES 'RANK-PAY'

'FUN' BECOMES 'UN-FAY'

'SKATEBOARD' BECOMES 'KATEBOARD-SAY'

GOT IT? CAN YOU FIGURE OUT WHAT IS BEING SAID BELOW?

OU-YAY AN-CAY EEP-KAY ECRETS-SAY OO-TAY!

ANSWER: YOU CAN KEEP SECRETS TOO!

SAFE SECRETS

you can either create your own code or use the ones below.

code 1 - mixed letters

you can make this code as individual as you like, simply mix up the letters of the alphabet so they actually stand in for another letter.

this could be one way to mix them up:

a	b	c	d	e	f	g	h	i	j	k	l	m	n	o	p	q	r	s	t	u	v	w	x	y	z
a	g	o	p	b	f	h	i	k	l	r	s	t	u	v	q	x	c	d	e	y	w	m	n	z	j

example:
you want to say: boys rule!
how the code makes it look: gvzd cysb!

code 2 - nifty numbers

This code is one you can use without a code breaker because you can always recite the alphabet to figure out what letter the number means!

a	b	c	d	e	f	g	h	i	j	k	l	m	n	o	p	q	r	s	t	u	v	w	x	y	z
1	2	3	4	5	6	7	8	9	10	11	12	13	14	15	16	17	18	19	20	21	22	23	24	25	26

example:

you want to say: no girls

how the code makes it look: 14.15 - 7.9.18.12.19

code 3 - secret symbols

If you ever want to make your secret message look like unimportant scribbles on a paper then use this code.

a	b	c	d	e	f	g	h	i	j	k	l	m	n	o	p	q	r	s	t	u	v	w	x	y	z
♋	♌	♍	♎	♏	⚹	♑	♒	♓	er	&	●	★	→	□	←	↓	↑	○	◇	◆	❖	∙	⊠	⊡	⌘

example:

you want to say: meet at the fort

how the code makes it look: ★ ● ● ◇   ♋ ◇   ◇ ● ●   ⚹ □ ↑ ◇

USING ONE OF THESE CODES WRITE YOUR OWN MESSAGE ON THE PIECE OF PAPER BELOW:

SECRET PLACES

Secret maps are important to spies, pirates, and explorers – or simply to keep track of the things you need to hide from your sister!

Use the space on the opposite page to create a map of your school, room, or hiding places that are only allowed to be known by you and your crew.

Keep a record of the symbols that you use (and keep it separate from your map!).

KEEP OUT

Things to mark down on your map:

- hiding place
- danger zone
- suspect seen
- treasure hidden
- meeting place

A Fun Game

Hide some 'treasure', create a map and see if your friends can figure it all out!

TIP: If you want to be ultra-sneaky don't draw a complete map – include just enough landmarks so only you and your mates can figure it out!

FILL IN THE DETECTIVE BLANKS

FILL IN THE BLANKS TO CREATE YOUR OWN EXCITING MYSTERY

TOP SECRET

I WAS WALKING HOME FROM SCHOOL WHEN OUT OF THE BLUE
.... JUMPED IN FRONT OF ME
AND.................................... BEFORE ....
COULD GET OUT OF HAND.................. TOLD ME THAT
.... HAD GONE MISSING. DESPERATE
TO FIND................ I ASKED FOR CLUES. APPARENTLY
.... HAD GONE MISSING AFTER ....
NO ONE NOTICED THAT .... WAS MISSING UNTIL
....

I REALIZED I WAS RUNNING OUT OF TIME. I RAN TO THE PHONE
AND CALLED .... AND ASKED FOR HELP.
.... WAS HAPPY TO HELP AND HAD A VERY
SPECIAL SKILL THAT WOULD BE PERFECT. ....'S
SPECIAL SKILL WAS .... AND THE WAY THEY
COULD HELP WAS ....

WE ARRIVED AT THE SCENE OF THE CRIME AND I IMMEDIATELY
SAW THE MOST IMPORTANT CLUE EVER ....
[FILL IN THE ENDING HERE] ....
....
....

FILL IN THE
SUPERHERO
BLANKS

My real name is ....
but what my friends don't know is that I am
also a superhero.

My superhero name is .... and
my main special power is ....

I use this power to ....
Even though that was my strongest power,
I also have other powers that help me out.
These other powers are .... ,
and ....
My favorite of these other powers is ....
.... because ....

When I am saving lives or helping someone out
I have to wear a disguise. My disguise is ....
....

I know I can't tell anyone my super secret, but
if I could, I would tell ....
.... for sure!

ME AND MY SPORTS SKILLS

Stick a photo or draw a picture of you doing your number one sport below. Don't forget to describe what you are doing on the opposite page so you can show your friends how cool you are!

DRAW IT HERE

STICK IT HERE

DESCRIBE YOUR AMAZING SPORT STUNT:

DESIGN SCHOOL ©™

Stand out from the crowd and design your own wicked skateboard!

You can get creative and come up with a fresh idea yourself, or you can blend together elements that already exist.

Get inspiration from everywhere: TV, magazines, nature, CD cases, book covers ... the list goes on and on.

get INDIVIDUAL

Why write your name on your things when you can come up with an awesome personal emblem that's all yours? Be sure to include things that are entirely YOU.

Hobbies

Favorite things

Matt Smith

Your name

Your favorite colors

Decorative elements that define you (sharp lines, soft rounds...)

DRAW YOUR EMBLEM HERE

CHUCKLE CORNER

Q. What's black and white and red all over?
A. A zebra with a rash!

Q. What do you say if you get into trouble for not doing your homework?
A. You can't yell at me for something I didn't do!

Q. Why did the boy tiptoe past the medicine cabinet?
A. He didn't want to wake the sleeping pills!

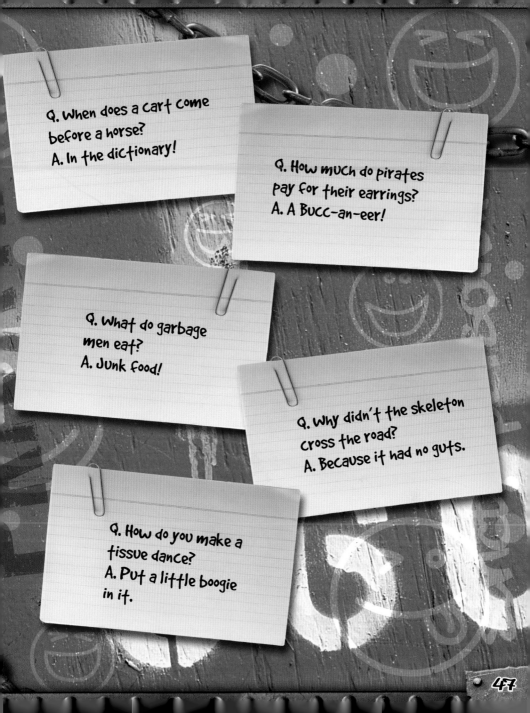

Q. When does a cart come before a horse?
A. In the dictionary!

Q. How much do pirates pay for their earrings?
A. A Bucc-an-eer!

Q. What do garbage men eat?
A. Junk food!

Q. Why didn't the skeleton cross the road?
A. Because it had no guts.

Q. How do you make a tissue dance?
A. Put a little boogie in it.

I DARE YOU

PARENTAL PERMISSION REQUIRED

Toughen up and show your mates you're not afraid of anything

Check off the dares below as you do them – and then dare your friends!

DARE	YOU	YOUR FRIEND
Eat a lemon raw		
Drink as much soda as you can		
April fool someone (tips on pages 60–61!)		

Create your own dares!

DARE	YOU	YOUR FRIEND

Remember: dares are supposed to test your courage, not your stupidity, so keep it safe!

CAUTION: DO NOT READ

TONGUE

Wrap your mouth around these tongue twisters and then challenge your friends! How many times can you say it without messing up?

Betty bought a bit of butter, but the butter was too bitter so Betty bought some other butter to make the bitter butter better!

TOP SCORE: _____

She sells sea shells by the sea shore.

TOP SCORE: _____

TWISTERS

Peter Piper picked a peck of pickled peppers.

TOP SCORE: _____

How much wood could a woodchuck chuck if a woodchuck could chuck wood?

TOP SCORE: _____

FACTS TO AMAZE YOUR FRIENDS WITH ...

Who says being a brainiac is hard??

1. An octopus has three hearts. It needs these, because it can't pump blood around its body as efficiently as a human heart.

2. The quietest noise we can hear is the movement in our eardrums.

WISH LIST

Realistic wishes
(Meaning ones that are definitely possible)

1. _____

2. _____

3. _____

4. _____

5. _____

6. _____

7. _____

8. _____

9. _____

10. _____

CRAZY WISH LIST

(If you could have ANYTHING, what would it be??)

1. _____

2. _____

3. _____

4. _____

5. _____

6. _____

7. _____

8. _____

9. _____

10. _____

CONFIDENTIAL

INVENT THIS!

Hi, my name is professor
....
and I would like to show you my latest invention.
I call it the..
....
and what it does is...
....
....
you could use it for...
....
Other details about your awesome new invention:
....
....
....
....

DRAW YOUR INVENTION HERE!

EXPLORE THIS!

If I were an explorer I would be like:

_____

_____

_____

I would search for:

_____

_____

_____

I want to find that because:

_____

_____

_____

_____

_____

My most useful explorer skill would be:

_____

_____

_____

The country I would want to check out would be:

_____

_____

_____

MY EXPLORER KIT

Every explorer needs to be prepared at all times!
Make a list of the things you will have to pack below.

1. _____
2. _____
3. _____
4. _____
5. _____
6. _____

APRIL FOOLS!

PARENTAL PERMISSION REQUIRED

The perfect prank for April fools can be hard to pull off, but if you put enough thought into it then whazam! — you can take home the title of 'the Joker'.

Prank Planning Checklist:

☐ Who are you trying to fool?

☐ Where will it happen?

☐ Do you need to organize anything before they get there?

☐ Is it safe?

WRITE THE DETAILS OF YOUR PLAN HERE!

CONFIDENTIAL